C000046749

FRED AND PENELOPE'S BOOK OF LOVE

Since Rupert Fawcett invented Fred twelve years ago Fred has become something of a star, with books and merchandise in several countries.

Fred's past life is documented in Rupert's thirteen previous books: *Fred, More Fred, The Extraordinary World of Fred, The Continued Adventures of Fred, Carry on Fred, At Home with Fred, Pure Fred, The One and Only Fred, The Little Book of Fred, The Best Bits of Fred, The Second Little Book of Fred, The Big Fat Fred Collection* and *The Third Little Book of Fred*.

Fred and Penelope's Book of Love contains nearly 200 cartoons – 100 of them completely new – revealing the strange intimacies of their marriage observed, as ever, by their black cat, Anthony.

Also by Rupert Fawcett published by Headline

CARRY ON FRED
AT HOME WITH FRED
PURE FRED
THE ONE AND ONLY FRED
THE LITTLE BOOK OF FRED
THE BEST OF FRED
THE SECOND LITTLE BOOK OF FRED
THE BEST BITS OF FRED
THE THIRD LITTLE BOOK OF FRED
THE BIG FAT FRED COLLECTION

FRED AND PENELOPE'S BOOK OF LOVE

Rupert Fawcett

HEADLINE

Copyright © 1990, 1991, 1992, 1993, 1994, 1995, 1996, 1997, 1998, 1999, 2000, 2001 Rupert Fawcett

The right of Rupert Fawcett to be identified as the Author
of the Work has been asserted by him in acccordance with the
Copyright, Designs and Patents Act 1988.

First published in 2001
by HEADLINE BOOK PUBLISHING

10 9 8 7 6 5 4 3 2 1

All rights reserved. No part of this publication may be
reproduced, stored in a retrieval system, or transmitted,
in any form or by any means without the prior written
permission of the publisher, nor be otherwise circulated
in any form of binding or cover other than that in which
it is published and without a similar condition being
imposed on the subsequent purchaser.

ISBN 0 7553 1018 7

Printed and bound in Italy by Canale & C.S.P.A

HEADLINE BOOK PUBLISHING
A division of Hodder Headline
338 Euston Road
London NW1 3BH

TRUE LOVE IS . . .

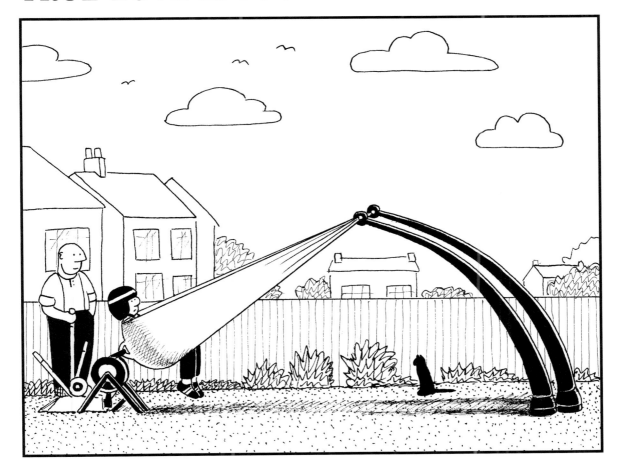

. . . helping her beat the traffic jams

TRUE LOVE IS . . .

... describing it to him when he hasn't seen it in a while

TRUE LOVE IS . . .

... holding down the quilt when you've
farted in bed

TRUE LOVE IS . . .

... taking full responsibility for giving her one glass of sherry too many

TRUE LOVE IS . . .

. . . trying not to laugh

TRUE LOVE IS . . .

. . . making sure his sandwich meets EU health regulations

TRUE LOVE IS . . .

. . . trying not to overreact to the telephone bill

TRUE LOVE IS . . .

... all going for walkies together

TRUE LOVE IS . . .

. . . letting her choose the holiday destination

TRUE LOVE IS . . .

. . . knowing when to stand back and say nothing

TRUE LOVE IS . . .

... tolerating his bad habits

TRUE LOVE IS . . .

. . . finding him sexy whatever he wears

TRUE LOVE IS . . .

. . . buying a tandem

TRUE LOVE IS . . .

. . . accepting that he is a lazy bum

TRUE LOVE IS . . .

. . . telling him baldness is a sign of virility

TRUE LOVE IS . . .

... taking pleasure in everything she does

TRUE LOVE IS . . .

... helping her out with her greenfly problem

TRUE LOVE IS . . .

. . . agreeing to let him pierce your navel to save money

TRUE LOVE IS . . .

... agreeing to help him test his human cannon

TRUE LOVE IS . . .

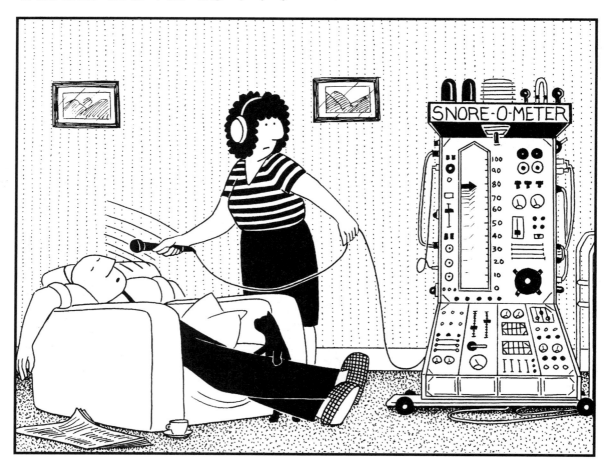

... *trying to get him into the* Guinness Book of Records

TRUE LOVE IS . . .

... going on adventure holidays together

TRUE LOVE IS . . .

. . . being sympathetic to her verbal diarrhoea

TRUE LOVE IS . . .

... encouraging her hobbies

TRUE LOVE IS . . .

. . . supporting his attempts at worm-charming

TRUE LOVE IS . . .

. . . letting him cheat at cards

TRUE LOVE IS . . .

. . . giving your guests an entertaining evening

TRUE LOVE IS . . .

. . . not feeling jealous when she shows affection to others

TRUE LOVE IS . . .

. . . accepting his love of DIY

TRUE LOVE IS . . .

... helping with the groceries

TRUE LOVE IS . . .

. . . trying to get used to the effects of his new vegetarian diet

TRUE LOVE IS . . .

. . . cooking a surprise dinner on her birthday

TRUE LOVE IS . . .

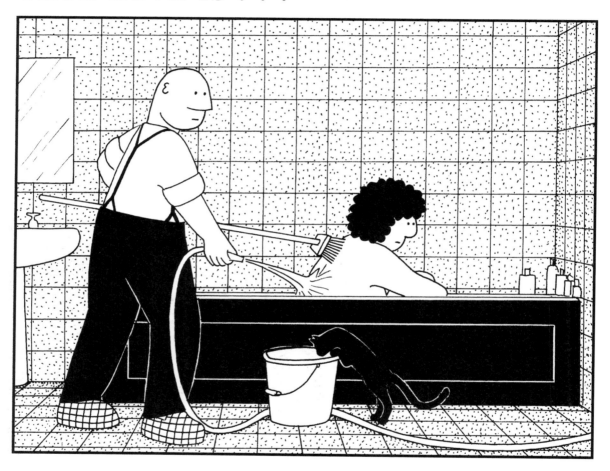

. . . scrubbing her back

TRUE LOVE IS . . .

... helping him get up in the morning

TRUE LOVE IS . . .

... telling her you still adore her despite the gradual appearance of crow's feet

TRUE LOVE IS . . .

. . . making sure she gets to her hairdressing appointment on time

TRUE LOVE IS . . .

. . . remaining calm when he reveals his true identity

TRUE LOVE IS . . .

... *having differences of opinion*

TRUE LOVE IS . . .

. . . a well choreographed morning routine

TRUE LOVE IS . . .

... not commenting on his drinking

TRUE LOVE IS . . .

. . . being able to drop your inhibitions

TRUE LOVE IS . . .

. . . making a granny annexe for her mother

TRUE LOVE IS . . .

*... telling him you understand how much
he hates Christmas shopping*

TRUE LOVE IS . . .

... telling him how much you are going to miss him when he goes upstairs to work on his computer

TRUE LOVE IS . . .

. . . letting him enjoy the adventure holiday in his own way

TRUE LOVE IS . . .

... not telling her you are losing the feeling in your legs

TRUE LOVE IS . . .

. . . aspiring to the same level of perfection

TRUE LOVE IS . . .

. . . bringing conflicts to a peaceful conclusion

TRUE LOVE IS . . .

. . . devoting a lot of time to choosing him the right birthday present

TRUE LOVE IS . . .

... calling the emergency services when she breaks a fingernail

TRUE LOVE IS . . .

... experimenting with new paint effects

TRUE LOVE IS . . .

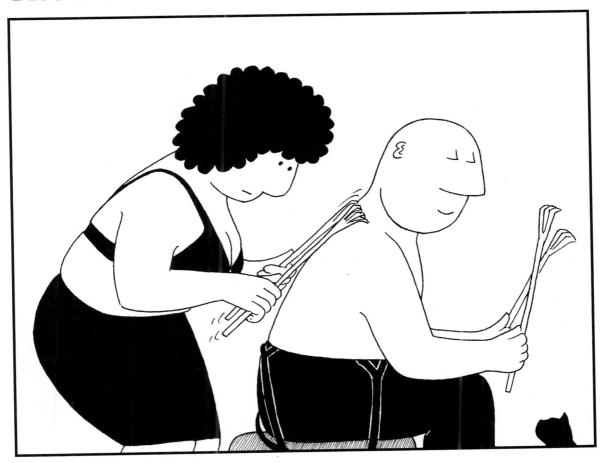

... giving each other a good scratch

TRUE LOVE IS . . .

. . . agreeing on the wisdom of safe sex

TRUE LOVE IS . . .

... helping him with his bad back

TRUE LOVE IS . . .

... supporting his efforts to make some extra money

TRUE LOVE IS . . .

... accepting that boys will be boys

TRUE LOVE IS . . .

... choosing to have frank and fair negotiations over who should have the last chocolate biscuit

TRUE LOVE IS . . .

. . . knowing when to look away

TRUE LOVE IS . . .

. . . working as a team

TRUE LOVE IS . . .

... trying to remain calm when she is making you late (again)

TRUE LOVE IS . . .

... enjoying getting out into the country together to stretch your legs

TRUE LOVE IS . . .

... telling him his is the biggest you've ever seen

TRUE LOVE IS . . .

. . . letting him dream his dreams of one day becoming a Chippendale

TRUE LOVE IS . . .

. . . sympathising when she has a bad-hair day

TRUE LOVE IS . . .

... *from time to time surprising him with a sensual new perfume*

TRUE LOVE IS . . .

. . . encouraging him to give up unhealthy habits

TRUE LOVE IS . . .

. . . saving her the effort of making her own breakfast

TRUE LOVE IS . . .

. . . remaining calm when she is pressing your buttons

TRUE LOVE IS . . .

. . . promising him that if he doesn't grow to love the new decor you'll change it back

TRUE LOVE IS . . .

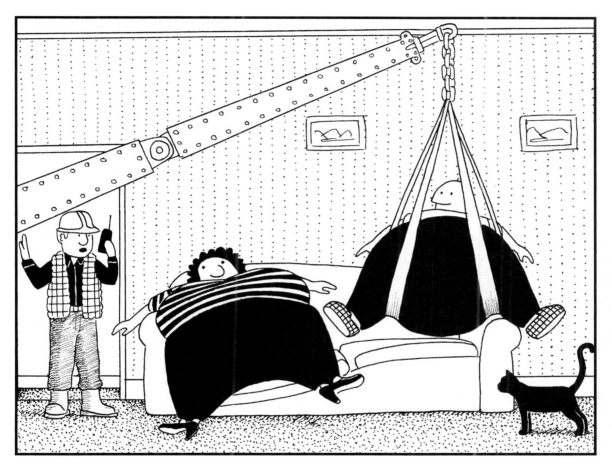

. . . jointly deciding to suspend your diets
for Christmas

TRUE LOVE IS . . .

. . . assuring him that you understand his feelings about the dentist

TRUE LOVE IS . . .

. . . helping her with her make-up

TRUE LOVE IS . . .

... not complaining about having to eat garden-furniture burgers again

TRUE LOVE IS . . .

. . . agreeing to give her driving lessons

TRUE LOVE IS . . .

... helping him with his over-sleeping problem

TRUE LOVE IS . . .

... *putting up with his peculiarities*

TRUE LOVE IS . . .

. . . letting him try to recapture his youth

TRUE LOVE IS . . .

. . . telling her you have eyes for her only

TRUE LOVE IS . . .

... digging and planting together

TRUE LOVE IS . . .

... always pretending you are hearing his favourite old joke for the very first time

TRUE LOVE IS . . .

. . . decorating the house together

TRUE LOVE IS . . .

. . . making him his favourite, upside-down cake

TRUE LOVE IS . . .

. . . trying to soothe her migraine with a little music

TRUE LOVE IS . . .

. . . allowing him to exercise his spirit of adventure

TRUE LOVE IS . . .

. . . accepting that you can't like all his hobbies

TRUE LOVE IS . . .

... calling him to tell him how much you miss him

TRUE LOVE IS . . .

... giving her breakfast in bed

TRUE LOVE IS . . .

... keeping a straight face when she shows you the results of her first art class

TRUE LOVE IS . . .

... re-living your honeymoon

TRUE LOVE IS . . .

. . . tolerating her love of animals

TRUE LOVE IS . . .

... having the car specially modified for the back-seat driver

TRUE LOVE IS . . .

. . . sharing country walks

TRUE LOVE IS . . .

. . . helping her out in the kitchen

TRUE LOVE IS . . .

... knowing when to turn a blind eye

TRUE LOVE IS . . .

... enjoying another evening in the fast lane

TRUE LOVE IS . . .

... attempting to share his enthusiasm for sport

TRUE LOVE IS . . .

. . . doing yoga together

TRUE LOVE IS . . .

... allowing her to use the house for a Chocoholics Anonymous convention

TRUE LOVE IS . . .

. . . pretending you don't mind when she wants to watch her favourite soap instead of the football

TRUE LOVE IS . . .

. . . sending each other romantic text messages

TRUE LOVE IS . . .

. . . putting up with his virtual baths

TRUE LOVE IS . . .

... telling her you find her new knickers incredibly sexy

TRUE LOVE IS . . .

. . . not blaming each other for taking the wrong exit off the M25

TRUE LOVE IS . . .

*... pretending not to notice the spot on
the end of her nose*

TRUE LOVE IS . . .

... letting him live out his SAS fantasies

TRUE LOVE IS . . .

... not interfering when he's cooking

TRUE LOVE IS . . .

DOWN WITH EVERYTHING

. . . supporting his political campaign

TRUE LOVE IS . . .

... being in tune with her menstrual cycle

TRUE LOVE IS . . .

. . . admiring his collection

TRUE LOVE IS . . .

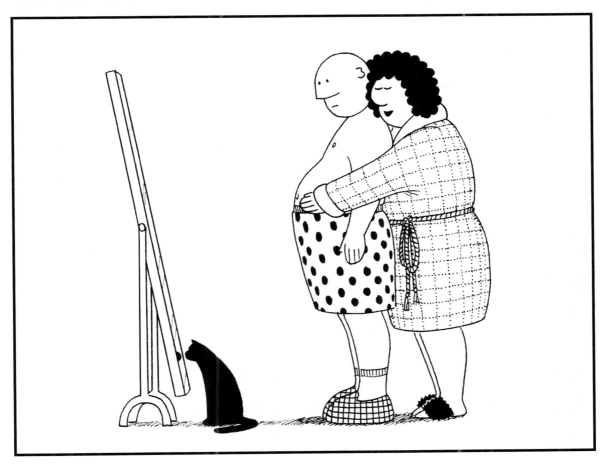

. . . telling him he's cuddly, not fat

TRUE LOVE IS . . .

... offering to help him research his forthcoming book, A Day in the Life of a Rolling-Pin

TRUE LOVE IS . . .

*... not being afraid to show your feelings
for each other in public*

TRUE LOVE IS . . .

. . . accepting his various peculiarities

TRUE LOVE IS . . .

... helping him look his best

TRUE LOVE IS . . .

. . . keeping your body in good shape
for him

TRUE LOVE IS . . .

. . . pretending to be interested in hearing all about her day

TRUE LOVE IS . . .

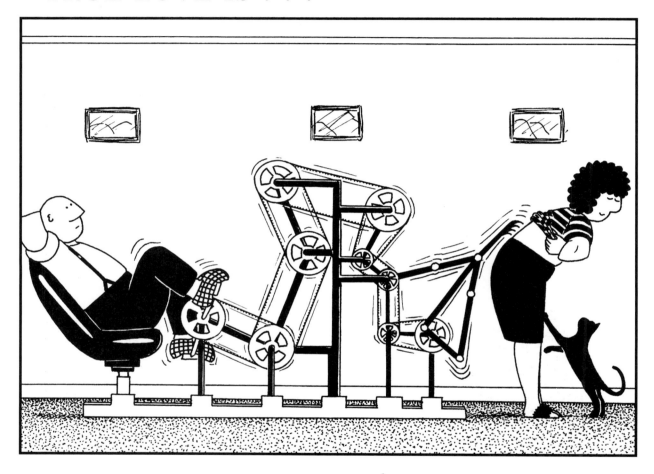

. . . giving her back a good scratch

TRUE LOVE IS . . .

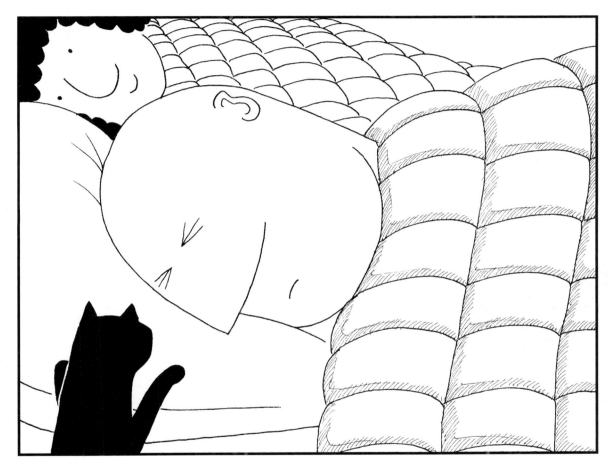

. . . letting her warm her feet on your back

TRUE LOVE IS . . .

... helping motivate him to cut the grass

TRUE LOVE IS . . .

. . . telling him you love him just as much as the cat

TRUE LOVE IS . . .

... admiring his inventions

TRUE LOVE IS . . .

. . . saying nothing about his breath in the mornings

TRUE LOVE IS . . .

... planning a keep-fit campaign together

TRUE LOVE IS . . .

... telling her she doesn't need make-up

TRUE LOVE IS . . .

. . . standing back while she prepares her breakfast

TRUE LOVE IS . . .

. . . letting her decorate the house exactly the way she wants

TRUE LOVE IS . . .

. . . knowing what turns her on

TRUE LOVE IS . . .

... telling her you can't stand skinny women

TRUE LOVE IS . . .

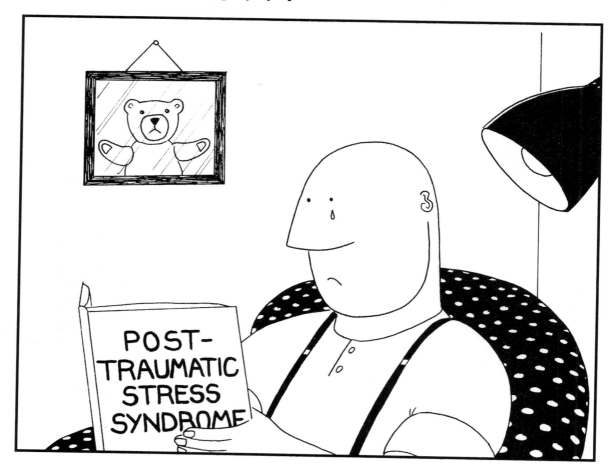

. . . allowing him time to grieve after the loss of his favourite teddy

TRUE LOVE IS . . .

... leaving the room prior to farting

TRUE LOVE IS . . .

. . . taking pride in his achievements

TRUE LOVE IS . . .

. . . giving her the pleasure of squeezing a blackhead

TRUE LOVE IS . . .

... giving her her first mobile phone

TRUE LOVE IS . . .

... agreeing to let her drive the new car

TRUE LOVE IS . . .

. . . getting out into the countryside on your exercise bikes

TRUE LOVE IS . . .

. . . disagreeing when she tells you she has put on weight

TRUE LOVE IS . . .

... nightly flossing sessions

TRUE LOVE IS . . .

... saying nothing about the crumbs on her side of the bed

TRUE LOVE IS . . .

. . . enjoying reading to each other

TRUE LOVE IS . . .

. . . putting up with his feet

TRUE LOVE IS . . .

. . . teamwork

TRUE LOVE IS . . .

. . . taking it on trust when she tells you bad taste is cool

TRUE LOVE IS . . .

. . . letting her hold the remote

TRUE LOVE IS . . .

. . . not commenting on his driving

TRUE LOVE IS . . .

. . . telling him size doesn't matter

TRUE LOVE IS . . .

. . . sharing Lottery night

TRUE LOVE IS . . .

... telling him he has a fantastic sense of humour

TRUE LOVE IS . . .

. . . not wanting to change anything about him

TRUE LOVE IS . . .

. . . agreeing that it's probably Chinese flu when you know it's just a cold

TRUE LOVE IS . . .

. . . making an effort with her mother

TRUE LOVE IS . . .

. . . offering to help raise money for her favourite charity

TRUE LOVE IS . . .

... waiting until she has left the room before adding salt

TRUE LOVE IS . . .

*... pretending you can't hear the noise
she is making in the toilet*

TRUE LOVE IS . . .

... not making a fuss about the weighing scales

TRUE LOVE IS . . .

. . . saying nothing about the
chocolate binge

TRUE LOVE IS . . .

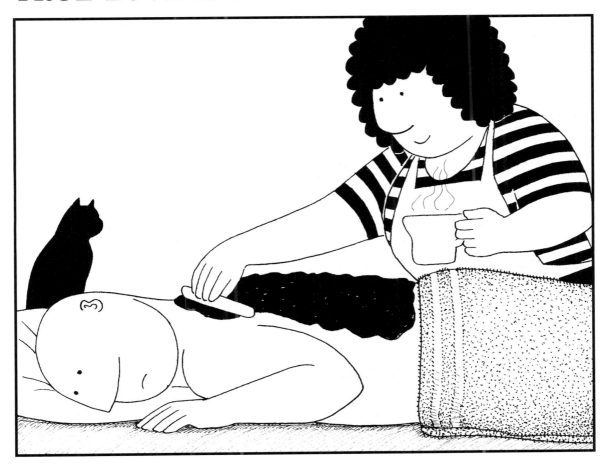

. . . letting her wax your back

TRUE LOVE IS . . .

. . . not making any comments about her diet

TRUE LOVE IS . . .

... never giving up in your search for her G-spot

TRUE LOVE IS . . .

. . . not looking at other women on the beach

TRUE LOVE IS . . .

. . . his and hers toilets

TRUE LOVE IS . . .

... agreeing that it would be fun to take a different route home from the supermarket

TRUE LOVE IS . . .

. . . only fighting under controlled conditions

TRUE LOVE IS . . .

... pretending you've caught the spider when it's actually still hiding somewhere under the bed

TRUE LOVE IS . . .

... agreeing to let him enter you for the Highland games wife-tossing competition

TRUE LOVE IS . . .

... letting her finish first when you go out jogging

TRUE LOVE IS . . .

... acting as though buying an animal
a Christmas present is perfectly
sane behaviour

TRUE LOVE IS . . .

. . . agreeing to let him do the plumbing to save money

TRUE LOVE IS . . .

. . . saying nothing when you discover her secret stash

TRUE LOVE IS . . .

... warming her lavatory seat

TRUE LOVE IS . . .

. . . waiting patiently while she puts on her face

TRUE LOVE IS . . .

*... telling him you love your toast
well done*

TRUE LOVE IS . . .

. . . not telling her the flowers cost you an arm and a leg

TRUE LOVE IS . . .

... going along with his jumbo-jet fantasy

TRUE LOVE IS . . .

. . . giving her seconds

TRUE LOVE IS . . .

... taking the taps end

TRUE LOVE IS . . .

... sharing a little prayer before opening the bank statement

TRUE LOVE IS . . .

. . . saying nothing about her first grey hair

TRUE LOVE IS . . .

. . . resisting using the phrase
'midlife crisis'

TRUE LOVE IS . . .

. . . not becoming upset by his lawn-rage

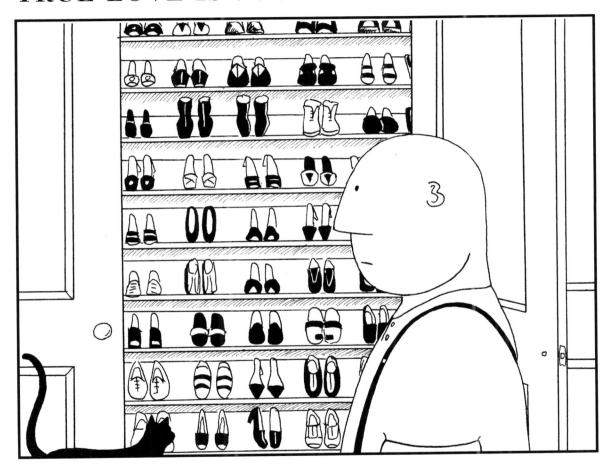

TRUE LOVE IS . . .

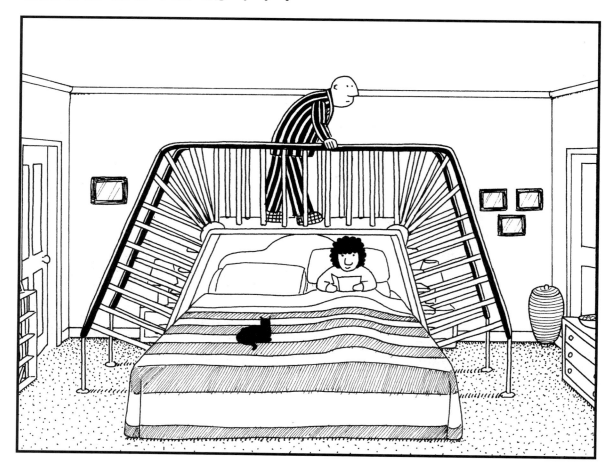

. . . giving him permission to build a short-cut to the bathroom

TRUE LOVE IS . . .

... letting her use your tools

TRUE LOVE IS . . .

. . . going to great lengths to fulfil her birthday request for a pair of mules

TRUE LOVE IS . . .

... identical ring-tones

TRUE LOVE IS . . .

... giving him a treat for helping with the groceries

TRUE LOVE IS . . .

... eating her chilli con carne when you know exactly what the results will be